KU-165-563

BALLYCLARE NURSERY SCHOOL
GRANGE DRIVE
BALLYCLARE
BT39 9EY
TEL. 028 9335 2982

Feet Are Not for Kicking

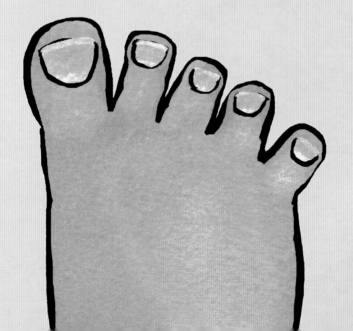

Look at those feet!
Aren't they sweet?

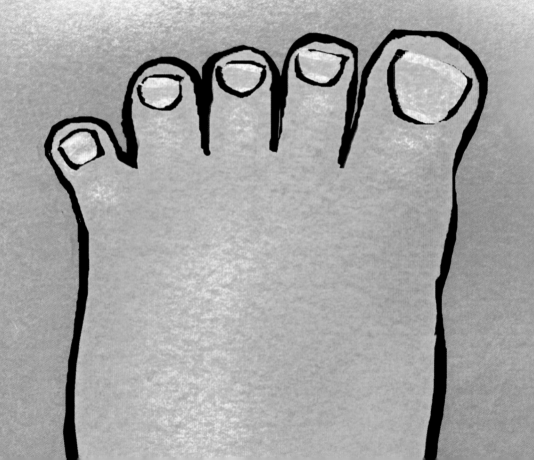

Ten little toes, all in a row.

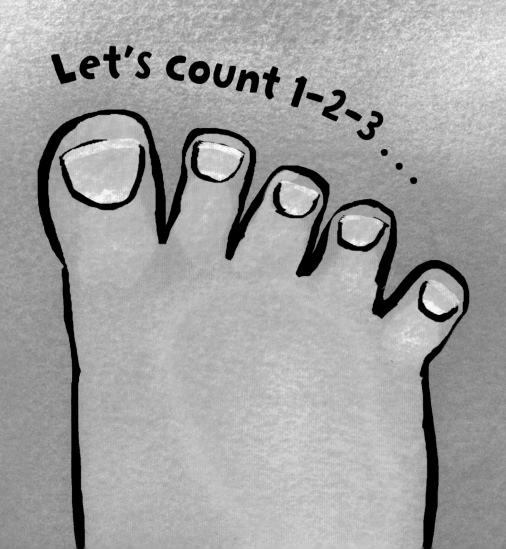

Let's count 1-2-3 . . .

What are feet for?

Walking

and landing

Running

and jumping

Climbing

and swinging

Feet are not
for kicking
people.

If you want to kick,
what can you kick?

A big ball . . .

a little ball . . .
            or leaves on the ground.

If someone
kicks you,
what can
you do?

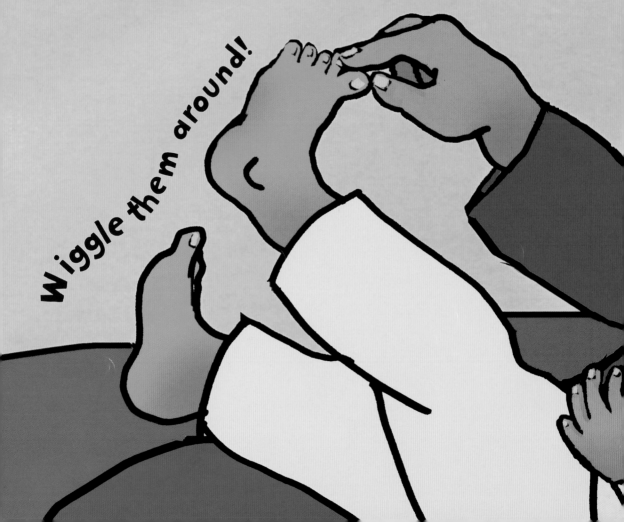

Ten little toes,
all in a row.

Feet are not
for kicking
someone. . .

...feet are
for FUN!

Tips for Parents and Caregivers

Toddlers are bundles of energy, and they love to run, jump, tumble, and explore all the wonderful things that their legs and feet help them do. But these little explorers are often unpredictable: one moment they're smiling and the next they're throwing a tantrum – complete with screaming, crying, and kicking.

When children this age are angry or frustrated, they tend to lash out with their voices, hands, and feet. These explosive moments are normal, but when they happen, someone might get hurt. Toddlers need help understanding that hurting others isn't okay. We can teach them that feet are not for kicking people – because kicking hurts. And we can reinforce this message by emphasising all the positive things our feet let us do.

Tips for positive behaviour

- Watch for signs that a child may be frustrated, cranky, angry, tired, or distressed – times when kicking is more likely to occur. Step in before kicking begins.

- Stay calm when tantrums happen. If a child is kicking and flailing, move him or her to a safe place so no one gets hurt. Holding a thrashing toddler may or may not help – it depends on the child. Do your best to speak softly and express empathy until the tantrum subsides.

- If a child kicks someone, you can use the phrase "Feet are not for kicking people." Say it gently and kindly, without shouting or scolding. You might add: "Ouch! Kicking hurts."

- Help energetic little ones stay active throughout the day, so they're less likely to use their feet to hurt someone else. Give them plenty of opportunities to run, jump, climb, dance, ride a tricycle – and, of course, kick a ball!

First published in the UK in 2008 by A & C Black
an imprint of Bloomsbury Publishing Plc
50 Bedford Square, London, WC1B 3DP

ISBN 978-1-4081-1072-0

All rights reserved. No part of this publication may be reproduced, stored in a retrieval
system or transmitted in any form, electronic, mechanical, photocopying, recording or
otherwise, without prior permission of Bloomsbury Publishing Plc.

A CIP catalogue record for this book is available at the British Library.

Text copyright © 2008 Elizabeth Verdick
Illustration copyright © 2008 Marieka Heinlen
Copyright © 2008 A & C Black

Original edition © 2006 by Free Spirit Publishing Inc., Minneapolis, U.S.A.,
http://www.freespirit.com under the title: Best Behaviour: Feet are not for Kicking.
All rights reserved under International and Pan-American Copyright Conventions.

Printed in China by Leo Paper Products

FSC
www.fsc.org
MIX
Paper from
responsible sources
FSC® C020056

7 9 10 8

BLOOMSBURY is a registered trademark of Bloomsbury Publishing Plc